Charles Terry Treadway

Young Father Time:

A Yankee Portrait

Eli Terry.

Young Father Time:

A Yankee Portrait

BY

BARROWS MUSSEY

MEMBER OF THE NEWCOMEN SOCIETY

BOSTON

NEW YORK · SAN FRANCISCO · MONTREAL

THE NEWCOMEN SOCIETY IN NORTH AMERICA

1950

PRINTED IN THE UNITED STATES OF AMERICA
BY PRINCETON UNIVERSITY PRESS FOR
THE NEWCOMEN PUBLICATIONS IN NORTH AMERICA

A DEDICATION

THIS Newcomen book is dedicated to my wife, Isabella, who, because of her deep interest in Early American glass, furniture, and pewter, has been my inspiration in gathering the data from which the Author has prepared this text. The illustrations are of clocks in my possession and of historical buildings related to the life of my great-great-grandfather, of whose life and times this tale is written. It is my hope that this story of early American Industry may be an inspiration to our readers in these times when we seem to have lost so much of the spirit, character, and stout-heartedness of our forebears.

—CHARLES TERRY TREADWAY

Bristol, Connecticut
September 1950

CHAPTER I

Introducing Eli Terry

EVERY countryside puts its own mark on the people who live there. It is rare, indeed, in these times to be able to point to a man who had so large a part in the early development of the whole region, but in this portrait we find such a man as the leader of men in the arts and crafts who had a large part in the transformation of central Connecticut from a region of scattered hill farms into an endless expanse of humming factories, and one who by his ingenuity and inventive genius turned a whole nation of men and women who had told time largely by the sun and the sundial into clock-watchers, many of them probably being able to read the dial and tell the time of day even before they knew the alphabet.

This man, therefore, is the man to whom this work gives credit for being the leader among the pioneers in mass production. We admit that there is probably a chance that many of our readers will never have heard of him before. His name was Eli Terry. His inventive genius and craftsmanship in large measure created the American clock industry, of course with the help of his apprentice boys and the tumbling brooks of Plymouth, Connecticut.

From his successors and imitators, along with those who concurrently had in a lesser way been making clocks in limited quantities, came nearly all the industry that now distributes not only clocks, but springs, locks, brass and brass castings, and even ball bearings in endless abundance from the Farmington, Naugatuck and Pequabuck valleys out to the five continents. It is quite amazing to see how much of this development can be traced back over just a few generations to Eli Terry's little woodshed shop on Warner's (now Plymouth) Hill in Plymouth.

Though Eli Terry had much to do in making present-day central Connecticut industry, it is just as true that an earlier and more rugged Connecticut made Eli Terry what he was.

The modern Nutmeg State takes a jocular pride in its legendary smartness at selling anything, even wooden nutmegs and horn gunflints; but the nickname is not very old. Eli Terry's peddlers largely helped to earn it. A century and a half ago Connecticut was invariably called "the land of steady habits."

The very peddlers who were already infesting Ohio and Virginia tried to look sedate at home in Waterbury or Berlin. A Connecticut divine boomed, "The morals of Waterbury are not on a high scale," feeling that the peddlers were corrupted by their trips to pioneer territory.

What he really approved of was a place like East Windsor, in the heart of old-fashioned Connecticut. "The people appear to have formed a settled character, which seems unlikely to be soon changed by their descendants. They have ever been distinguished for a steady, industrious character, and orderly habits; and are unquestionably a valuable collection of citizens."

At East Windsor on the Connecticut River Eli Terry was born, April 13, 1772. His father farmed and was a tanner on the side. No doubt wandering shoemakers and saddlers bought leather from Samuel Terry before starting their round of visits to outlying farms. Our clergyman remarks, "In few places, where so many people are collected, is an aspect so entirely rural presented everywhere to the eye of the traveler."

Terry's own life is a scale model of what he helped bring about in Connecticut and the whole eastern United States. He began with nothing, made his own way to the top, and retired in middle age on three thousand a year, rich beyond his dreams; but he could never quite leave clocks alone.

He started as a farm boy in a rustic village whose "many people" numbered almost three thousand, which made it the seventh largest town in the state; it was so important in its quiet way that we are startled to find it the home of Podunk Brook and the fierce Podunk Indian tribe. How Eli went from farming through craftsmanship to manufacturing and true riches, I am now about to set forth.

Among the functions of the Windsor selectmen ever since 1650 had been that of making sure every child and apprentice in town was taught to read, write, and ply some useful trade or calling; they could assume charge of any child whose parents neglected this duty.

The Terry family, however, needed no such nudging for their eldest son. The Revolution may have held back Eli's schooling, but more likely improved it—Windsor was a center for British and Hessian prisoners of war, whose officers ran horse-races in East Windsor, and many of whose Hessian enlisted men fraternized and settled near by after the war.

From friend or ex-enemy, Eli Terry learned to write a flourishing hand that puts modern under-water penmanship to shame; and in 1786, very likely about his fourteenth birthday, he began his apprenticeship at a "useful trade."

Daniel Burnap of East Windsor, who had learned his business at Norwich from the great Thomas Harland, undertook, in return for the next seven years of Eli's faithful service, to feed, clothe, and house him, and teach him clockmaking.

The trade of clockmaking in 1786, though useful, was not desperately busy. It was a one-man, one-at-a-time craft for skilled fingers, not an industry. The industry still waited for Eli Terry to create it.

A normal household told time by the noon mark drawn on the kitchen windowsill. Such a country town as Lebanon, Connecticut, boasted only thirteen wooden clocks and seven brass ones; eight years later, in 1794, the more prosperous center of Guilford had thirty-five wooden and fifty-four brass clocks—all, of course, what we call grandfather clocks. A tall clock in the house marked you as a person of substance, like a tall piano a hundred years later.

The moment when Eli Terry himself starts learning about clocks is a good opening for me to explain what little you should know in order to appreciate Eli.

Every clock is a machine with power to keep it going (the "time train") and some device to keep it from going too fast (the "controlling mechanism," governed by an "escapement"). If the clock is to strike the hours, it has another set of wheels, with their own source of power, called the "striking train." The old clockmakers spoke of a *clock* when it had a striking train, of a *timepiece* when it had not.

The case, though often expensive and beautiful, was wholly unimportant to the actual timekeeper. Often a cabinetmaker put a case on a movement brought to him by someone who had first bought the clock, then saved up for the casing-in. Many Connecticut clocks were simply hung on the wall without any case—the "wag-on-the-wall" of old stories.

The power that drives the clock nowadays may be electricity, a coiled spring, or a weight on a cord. In Eli Terry's day the weight was the only power in use for clocks; springs were nearly confined to watches and the newly invented chronometers, and it was only Terry's successors and offshoot concerns in central Connecticut who discovered how to make springs cheap and good enough for cheap clocks. Electricity did not keep time until 1860.

Hundreds of escapements have been invented to prevent the clock hands from running away; but the odds-on favorite, universal in Terry's day, is the pendulum. (And by the way, the clock weights drive the pendulum; the pendulum doesn't drive the clock.)

You probably knew this much without my telling you; about the next point you may never have thought at all unless you collect antiques.

The cogwheels and gears of all modern clocks are metal, generally brass. When you find a clock with wooden wheels, then, it is obviously a curiosity: one might naturally guess it must be so old that the maker scarcely knew how to work brass.

Yet some antique-fancying friend is quite likely to inform you, with a superior smile, that the wooden works only prove it is machine-made, and not old at all.

Neither notion is true. Brass-wheeled clocks were the normal product of English and American clockmakers until after 1750. Practically every early American clockmaker could cast his own brass parts—if he could find the brass. And any wooden-wheeled clock that you are likely to see outside a museum was produced by machinery after 1807; yet wooden clockworks have been made, probably, for almost four hundred years. There are even seventeenth-century German wooden watches.

So far as Eli Terry goes, the wooden works bring into our story a large family named Cheney (later famous as silk manufacturers) in East Hartford, the next town to East Windsor. The original Benjamin Cheney was a universal mechanic, a carpenter and millwright who ran a sawmill but would tackle anything wooden, clocks included. His sons Benjamin and Timothy made a career of wooden clock-building. They produced each clock individually, like a brass one, only they cut the toothed wheels out of wood, with compasses, dividers, a fine saw, and perhaps a foot lathe, instead of casting them out of brass, and notching the teeth with a "clock-maker's engine." Wood-working was second nature to the Cheneys, and they could get their oak, cherry, and laurel raw material from the old sawmill, whereas brass was a scarce article usually imported from unfriendly England. The Cheneys and their numerous sons made so many wooden-wheeled clocks that the characteristic product is sometimes called a "Cheney movement." Though the works were wood, the dials were handsomely engraved brass: a wooden dial on wooden works was a later idea.

The Cheneys were in full swing when Eli Terry bound himself out to Daniel Burnap. But Eli first had to get through the floor-sweeping and fire-building stage of apprenticeship, and then to learn about brass-wheeled clocks, which were what Burnap dealt in. Eli learned to turn his own screws, draw his own wire, and make the tools he would need when he set up for himself as a clockmaker.

Even by Eli's time a clockmaker could get on with less varied skill than twenty years before. You could go out and buy most of the tools a clockmaker needed. Burnap, for example, made his own lathes, taps, and dividers; his engraver's and wood-working tools he bought.

Just about then, too, Connecticut clockmakers largely gave up brass-founding, and took to buying brass parts from such foundries as the Doolittle plant at Hartford. When Burnap was first apprenticed to Thomas Harland, clockmakers had to be at home in every kind of mechanics; by the time he moved away from East Windsor in 1800, all that the ordinary clockmaker did was to buy and put together wheels.

Eli Terry, obviously, did not take the easy way. When he got through with Burnap he could make or repair brass-wheeled clocks, and he could make the tools to make them. Building wooden movements was considered a humble sort of trade around Windsor, but nevertheless Eli went to one of the Cheneys for instruction in the fine points. Benjamin Cheney had already taught clockmaking to the first of the Willard dynasty that ruled the trade in Massachusetts, and (after a fashion) to the eccentric John Fitch of East Windsor. (Fitch was one of several inventors who preceded Fulton in building practical steam-boats.) Benjamin or Timothy seems to have done better by Eli, because no one could ever say that Eli went away ignorant of wooden clock movements.

The last step in Eli Terry's education is a fighting subject among clock historians. Since I do not know any better than they do what actually happened, I shall make bold to guess that Burnap sent his promising apprentice, young Terry, over to his own old master at Norwich. Thomas Harland, having learned clockmaking in England, could put a final polish on a young artisan's work such as no inland training could give. Harland ran a large shop, with both apprentices and journeymen; his equipment alone was valued in 1795 at the tremendous sum of $1500. And even if Eli never visited Harland, he must have had his glory at second hand from Burnap, who was remembered as one of Harland's outstanding pupils.

The seven (or maybe six) years of Eli Terry's apprenticeship brought more changes than just the decline of craftsmanship in clockmaking—in 1786 the Continental Congress agreed to have a Federal coinage, but very little of it got around; that November times were so hard in Massachusetts that Daniel Shays led an armed rebellion only twenty-five miles up-river from East Windsor. On September 17 of the next year, the state delegates agreed that the new United States Constitution should take effect Wednesday, March 1, 1789. Connecticut, which ratified the Constitution by a vote of 128 to 40, showed more enthusiasm than New York (30 to 28) or laggard Rhode Island (34 to 32, and two years late). In 1788 Washington was elected president, the District of Columbia and the town of Cincinnati were established, cotton was first planted in Georgia, and the half-taught clockmaker John Fitch launched his first steamboat on the Delaware River.

The year 1789 probably did not impress a seventeen-year-old 'prentice lad so much as it does us; still, Washington was inaugurated and the Federal Republic officially begun in March, and that should have been almost as exciting as the opening game of the season is now. The first Congress met in April; Oliver Ellsworth, the leading light of Windsor, was a senator from Connecticut.

By 1790 Eli had long since graduated from sweeping and errand-running, and might be taking an interest in things that would soon affect his livelihood as a journeyman clockmaker. The first census found 3,929,326 people in the new Union; the mathematical center of this population was twenty-three miles east of Baltimore. In 1791 Congress incorporated the Bank of the United States for $10,000,000 in the capital city of Philadelphia. Benedict Arnold died abroad, mourned by none in his native Connecticut.

Eli should not have been a free journeyman, "out of his time," until 1793, but apparently he may have mounted that step the year before. Good masters were sometimes generous to good apprentices.

So far as East Windsor went, a new local boy making clocks probably drew quite as much notice as the badly needed reorganization of the Post Office or the admission of Kentucky to the Union. Eli was too young to help re-elect George Washington.

He was not too young, though, to make some tall clocks that connoisseurs today are exceedingly proud to own. I have called his career a schematic chart of American clockmaking, and this is a high point. He had learned to make tall, brass-wheeled clocks as carefully and as well as the best masters in America could teach him. All the old Connecticut of steady habits was in his marrow: for the rest of his life he ate sparingly, shunned both liquor and tobacco, and eschewed gambling (which his own success was to make practically synonymous with Connecticut clockmaking). All his life, too, he kept his keen eye for good workmanship. He produced it himself, and respected it in others.

The fine clocks of the old fashion that twenty-one-year-old Eli turned out bore handsome brass dials engraved, according to some experts, by Daniel Burnap for his protege; other authorities merely see Burnap's influence strong upon the hand of Terry. Certainly you need little imagination to find a likeness between Eli Terry's signature and the "E. Terry" engraved in script across the dial. The dial of Eli's masterpiece (the first clock that proved him a master of his trade) is said to have been beaten from a kettle.

Such tall clocks as Eli or Burnap made were produced in an economy of scarcity. They were expensive, turned out to order for some local squire who dropped in and stated his wants. The word *salesmanship* would have been Chinese to anyone in East Windsor. Clocks were not sold, they were bought.

As for the small wares carried afar by the peddlers, what decent man would be a peddler? "Many of the young men, employed in this business," said President Dwight of Yale, "part, at an early period with both modesty, and principle. Their sobriety is exchanged for cunning; their honesty for imposition; and their decent behaviour for coarse impudence. Mere wanderers, accustomed to no order, control, or worship; and directed solely to the acquisition of petty gains; they soon fasten upon this object; and forget every other, of a superior nature. The only source of their pleasure, or their reputation, is gain; and that, however small, or however acquired, secures both. No course of life tends more rapidly, or more effectually to eradicate every moral feeling."

Eli's pious horror will hardly have gone so far as "old Pope Dwight's," but he had enough of the artisan in him so that he always thought first about making clocks, second about selling them. His sons learned to reverse that order.

In 1793 the inevitable close connection between making clocks and selling them was the other way around from what it is now: unless you could start with a buyer, you simply could not make the clock. No one knows for sure why Eli Terry left sedate old East Windsor, and rode his horse across rivers and rocks to the new, thinly settled Northbury parish in Watertown. But would you have stayed, with a Burnap in the prime of life at home, and a Cheney behind every bush of East Hartford? Go west, and grow up with the country!

A little after Eli's time, New England clockmakers would sometimes move their businesses as much as a day's journey by wagon. But in 1793 wagons were scarce; the first American-built carriage was a dozen years away; in a horse trade you still urged that your animal could swim like a fish. Eli will have done well to afford a horse and saddle.

Some thirty-five miles to southwestward—an awfully good day's journey—lay the little parish called Northbury, then in

Watertown, which in turn had belonged to Waterbury until 1780. Eli Terry turned up here on the first Monday of September, 1793. Either he arrived late at night or he had broken his journey at sundown on Saturday; he was not the reprobate to profane the Sabbath.

It was no great puzzle why Eli left East Windsor; why he pitched on Northbury is another question. Possibly he had been there before. A guess as good as any is that he had been, and had struck up an acquaintance with a girl named Eunice Warner, whose family was among the most prominent in Northbury. The tremendous hill from modern Plymouth down to Thomaston was long called Warner's Hill after Eunice's grandfather; Northbury without Warners, Blakeslees, and Fenns would have been practically unthinkable. Perhaps old man Warner felt, conversely, that Warners without Northbury were impossible. Anyone who really wanted Eunice had better come around where she was.

Whether Eli's choice of Northbury was cause or effect, he came where Eunice was. The next we know about him, he was scratching for a living there—making clocks, repairing clocks and watches, and engraving on metal. He even kept a stock of spectacles for sale. New as the country was, a good clockmaker named Gideon Roberts had already begun producing wooden movements only five or six miles away in Bristol; Litchfield South Farms and Southington likewise had active men at work. James Harrison of Southington made brass clocks with enameled dials, and had sold his first three in January and February of 1791. Two of them brought him £4 each—fifteen of the new dollars that had not yet come into circulation.

The state of the Union in 1793 favored trade more than manufacture. By maintaining strict neutrality in the embargo feud between France and England, the United States managed to appropriate nearly all the carrying trade of Europe. Shipping and shipbuilding were so profitable in the next twenty years that manufacturing did not attract capital. For all our lack of wheeled vehicles, we were already perhaps the world's most commercial nation per capita.

One good thing about wooden clocks: the capital investment was small. It was twenty years before either outgo or income made

Eli Terry at all prominent among the tradespeople of his new home. For nearly a decade he scarcely even tried to sell clocks away from there.

He had other matters on his mind. On the twelfth of March, 1795, he married Eunice Warner, and the young Terrys set up housekeeping in a house on Town Hill; tradition says their furniture was one chair and one cup and saucer apiece. It was enough to get Eli in under the wire as a householder and taxpayer less than two months later, when Northbury gained its independence from Watertown.

On the eighth of May the Connecticut legislature incorporated the former parish of Northbury as the town of Plymouth; there were 294 taxpaying incorporators, including Eli Terry and a whole flock of his inlaws. The present town of Thomaston and the village of Terryville were both in Plymouth, and both owe their existence to Eli at one remove.

Throughout 1796 Eli simply worked away at tall-clock movements, brass and wooden. I hardly think he went off peddling, because Eunice had their first child, Anna, three days before Christmas.

The next year his mind was bubbling with a great invention—an "equation clock." The equation it made was between apparent, or sun, time (which differs with each day in the year) and mean time, which is the standard nowadays, when everyone has a clock. Mean time in a given locality is determined by a theoretical average day, and does not vary summer or winter. The distinction has been forgotten by you and me along with the ability to judge time by the sun; but even thirty years later one of Eli's equation clocks still started a brisk public row in New Haven.

Eli said of his invention: "Said improvement consists in showing the apparent together with the mean time and the difference between each; having two minute hands, turning on the same center. One of which being of a different color and pattern (that it may be distinguished) shows the mean or true time, the same as common clocks; the other together with the striking part and hour hand shows the apparent time, as divided by the sun according to the table of the variation of the sun and clock for each day in the year. The said improvement diminishes from, more than it adds to the friction of the clock, and it is not more liable to disorder than common clocks." On November 27, 1797, President John Adams signed Terry's patent—the first clock patent issued by the new United States Patent Office. Of course there had been other clock inventions, such as the wind-powered self-winding steeple clock of Benjamin Hanks in near-by Litchfield; but Hanks's 1783 patent came only from the Connecticut legislature.

Eli's first patent was the only one he never had any trouble over—no infringements, no lawsuits, no squabbles. And no profits. The rich city customers who wanted glossy tall clocks with chimes, moon's phases, calendars, and such ingenuities were not going to ford half the rivers of Hartford County to get them. In 1800 Eli advertised one of his equation clocks for sale; but no collector since has ever set eyes on it.

It must have been about then that Eli realized the fording of streams had better be done by the clockmaker, not his customer. You made just one equation clock, and waited to sell it. Of wooden movements you could risk a few more. Four was a handy number: one for each saddlebag, one lashed dial outward to the pommel of the saddle, one on the cantle. This was a larger stock than that of William Pattison, the first Berlin tin-peddler, who had carried his wares in a basket. And indeed a saddle-load at $25 per clock had more attractions even for a bred-in-the-bone craftsman than a patent on a beautiful contraption nobody wanted. Once you got beyond the bailiwick of the Waterbury and Litchfield clockmakers, you could find customers enough.

How they would pay you was another matter. Eli once took two saddlebags of salt pork for a clock. I imagine the swap was remembered because it was so natural, not as a curiosity. "Clock notes" signed by optimistic customers continued for forty years to be about the thinnest asset that a hard-driven clock manufacturer could raise money on. He had to employ a man who spent his whole time going around the country collecting notes; any other kind of note was better than a clock note.

It was while Eli Terry hopefully waited for someone to buy equation clocks that Eli Whitney at New Haven took the greatest single forward step ever made in American industry. Whitney was a real whittling, contriving Yankee, like Eli Terry, only more so.

As a small boy Whitney once shirked meeting to investigate the forbidden interior of his father's watch, and tradition says he got it apart and properly together again undetected. He took an interest in timepieces, at all events. Eli Whitney graduated from Yale probably within a few weeks of the time when Eli Terry graduated from apprentice clockmaking; Whitney went south, invented the cotton gin, promptly found out that Georgia liked his machine much better than it liked paying royalties to Yankee inventors, and so came back to a workshop at New Haven.

By 1798 Whitney had pretty much given up suing the whole south as a bad job, and instead had hit on a scheme for making muskets in enormous quantities. This was the great forward step in manufacturing: to think of each musket not as a unit, a firearm, but as the assemblage of many small parts from batches produced by machinery. The parts were to be made "as much like each other as the successive impressions of a copper-plate engraving." Then any apprentice lad could slap them together, and they would fit without trying or shaping. (If Whitney had but known it, this meant the end of all apprenticeship. "So easy did Mr. Whitney find it to instruct new and inexperienced workmen, that he uniformly preferred to do so, rather than to attempt to combat the prejudices of those, who had learned the business under a different system.")

No one really knows whether Whitney originated or borrowed the idea. Somebody in France apparently undertook to make muskets with interchangeable lock parts about 1785, and Thomas Jefferson wrote of it to John Jay; but anyhow the French never manufactured many arms in that way, and Whitney did.

The operation got off to a slower start than Whitney expected. He signed a contract in January of 1798 to deliver four thousand muskets by the end of September '99, and six thousand more within another year. Actually, however, he finished five hundred his first year, and took eight years to make the ten thousand. But the government was satisfied: interchangeable manufacture was a success.

Another thing nobody knows is whether Eli Terry learned directly from Eli Whitney. One old clockmaker who was born in Plymouth shortly after the great innovation, and knew Eli Terry well, wrote, "He soon invented a way of cutting the wheel teeth by machinery, which process it was said was hinted to him by Eli Whitney." Cutting teeth by machinery might have been merely a return to the clockmaker's brass-wheel "engine," but the same historian also tells about wire gauges that dropped past the work on the lathe when a piece was turned down to the right size. And a modern biographer seems to believe Whitney thought of interchangeable clock parts before he began actually producing muskets.

No matter where Eli Terry got the idea, he was well launched on machine clockmaking before Whitney had finished his musket contract. Terry, like Whitney, needed a contract before he could risk tooling up. Whitney persuaded the government to engage him; Terry was sought out by private businessmen who knew he was their only good source of supply.

Eli and Eunice Terry's second child and first son, the heir apparent Eli Jr., was born June 25, 1799. Within a year or so Eli (now entitled to the grave suffix of *Senior*) was employing two or three hands in his shop, and turning out probably a dozen or two wooden tall-clock movements at a time. The work was still being done cut-and-try, with compasses, saw, and file. (That, incidentally, was the year when the national capital was moved from Philadelphia to the new city of Washington. The center of the nation's population was still hard by, eighteen miles west of Baltimore.)

Eli would go out to the "New Country" west of the Hudson two or three times a year, offering his clock movements at $25 each. His competitor from Bristol, Gideon Roberts, went out in the same way, but as yet he was only finishing three or four at a time; later he "had to give up this kind of business; he could not compete with machinery."

Late in 1801 another future clockmaker and industrialist, Henry, was born to the Terrys. Tripoli declared war on the United States as soon as word crossed the Atlantic that the American navy was ordered reduced to thirteen vessels. But hostilities did not begin until 1802, when Terry had something much more important on his mind.

In 1802 he put water power to work. He built a small shop on the hill between Plymouth and what is now Thomaston, over a stream promisingly named Niagara Brook. And here the lathe began to replace the keyhole saw: the craft became an industry. "The manufacture of clocks by water power, for a wholesale trade, was this year commenced by Eli Terry; an enterprise regarded by many, as a rash adventure," said the first historian of American industry.

For a wholesale trade—there was the key to the matter. Eli Sr. had graduated from peddler to supplier of peddlers. Let someone else ford the streams and bring home the pork.

Not that Eli was rich. The Cape Cod salt works might return twenty-five per cent on their $130,000 investment; Eli's investment was probably not two per cent of that, and clockmaking had scarcely begun to flutter the farming town of Plymouth. It was 1805, and the next baby, little James, was over a year old before Eli made bold to think of starting twenty-five clocks in a batch. The tax assessors of Bristol had found only 48 householders with clocks in 1804, Gideon Roberts notwithstanding.

Late in 1806 Napoleon unintentionally gave Terry and all the other new American manufacturers a helping hand. When his Berlin Decree blockaded the British Isles and cut off American foreign commerce, industry boomed at home.

And in 1807, perhaps as a result, perhaps by chance, came the contract that, as I said before, launched Eli on mass production. Two brothers in Waterbury named Porter—Edward, the former Waterbury Congregational minister, and Levi, who had been making rolled-brass buttons—somehow got the insane idea that they could sell *four thousand* clock movements if they could buy them cheap enough.

Eli Terry with his water power was their man. Gideon Roberts, next door in Bristol, by now was making clocks in some quantity; but though he had plied his trade there ten years longer than Terry, he would not or could not risk this gamble for fortune.

"Mr. Terry," said one of his workmen, "was at that time making more clocks than any other man in the country, about two hundred in a year, which was thought to be a great number. My guardian, a good old man, told me that there was so many clocks then making, that the country would soon be filled with them, and the business would be good for nothing in two or three years . . ." In 1805 he heard some old gentleman at a training muster: "The foolish man, they said, had begun to make two hundred clocks; one said, He never would live long enough to finish them; another remarked, that if he did he never would, nor could possibly sell so many, and ridiculed the very idea."

By the ridiculous contract the Porters offered, they would supply the stock for four thousand wooden tall-clock movements, dials, and hands. Eli had three years to convert the stock into finished movements at four dollars per movement.

Four thousand wooden clocks was probably as many as the whole Connecticut industry had produced in any previous decade, and the price was a sixth of what Eli had been accustomed to getting. So he closed the deal, and started off by selling his mill to a former apprentice, Heman Clark, and buying another with more water.

The new plant was an old grist mill in a hamlet called Ireland, in southeastern Plymouth; Eli bought it of a local notable named Calvin Hoadley.

Hoadley was a carpenter, and had as an apprentice his nephew Silas Hoadley, who no doubt wielded hammer and saw in the job of converting the grist mill. Three years later, when just out of his time, Silas Hoadley was one of Terry's partners.

The first of February, 1807, Eunice Terry had her fifth child, Silas Burnham Terry, who grew up to be a clockmaker like the rest of the family.

Terry made no hasty fumbles at producing clocks; for a year he did nothing but plan and prepare. Probably the Porters were glad to let their oak and laurel stock season. And if Terry were late in finishing his four thousand clocks, that would be so much the longer before they need worry about paying him.

But in 1808 Terry showed that he did not propose to be late. He started a single batch of five hundred clocks through the plant. By the end of the year he had finished those and as many again.

In 1808, furthermore, Eli hired another young carpenter and joiner, Seth Thomas, from Wolcott, Conn. At first Thomas's job was "putting together" the clocks—fitting the various parts together, and setting one clock after another in running order. Thomas himself always remained a cabinetmaker at heart.

Evidently the rapid output of 1808 relieved Eli's mind enough so that he could start thinking about the next step. The clock movements in his contract, after all, were movements only, and the

Porters' peddler customers would sell them in that stripped form. What about reducing the size of the movement and the length of the pendulum, and selling the clock complete with a case small enough to stand on a shelf?

The conventional grandfather clock had a thirty-nine-inch pendulum whose swing took one second, whence it was called a "seconds pendulum." Eli's new short clock had a half-seconds pendulum, about ten inches long. In some the pendulum was pivoted to the left of center, like a recent American President. The shelf clock was still powered by weights, but Eli ingeniously ran the cords over pulleys at the upper instead of the lower corners of the movement.

Terry was only groping, and did not think much of his first mantel clocks, but people bought several hundred despite his doubts. He could see the signs of a new market, not through the Porters' eyes but from experience.

The people of Plymouth did not yet realize what Eli was doing to their town. A tax was levied in 1808 on forty-seven firms and persons engaged in "special occupations." The highest assessments were on four traders and an attorney, $100 each; next came a mill at $90, a physician at $67, an innkeeper and trader and a mill at $60, and an innkeeper and a clothier at $50 each. Twenty of the forty-seven paid a higher assessment than Eli Terry, who was down for twenty dollars (the average of the assessments was $32.50). Twenty-one assessments were less than Terry's, running down to five dollars for a mill. To the Plymouth tax listers Eli Terry was just a fellow with a smallish mill.

Events at home and abroad combined neatly with the stirrings in Eli's brain to render 1808 a turning point for him. The new and more stringent Embargo Act (reversed by wags into the "O grab me" Act) made foreign trade harder than ever; meanwhile Connecticut promoters had loosened up domestic travel by building, in about five years, some thirty-nine turnpikes extending 770 miles. True, even the turnpikes were mostly just cart-tracks or mud wallows, depending on the season; but they were beginning to be cart-tracks rather than bridle paths, and they did mark settled lines of communication. When you got mired, somebody might come the same way inside a day or two and help haul you out.

The Waterbury and Litchfield turnpike ran through Plymouth, passing by the land of a miller on the Naugatuck named John Sutliff, whom Eli Terry knew well. Sutliff was perfectly certain that he could find precious metals on his land if he dug far enough. He expected to dip up liquid gold and silver by the ladleful.

One day a traveler along the turnpike heard noises underfoot; evidently not having a consignment of clocks to turn over, he took time out for investigation. "Having obtained assistance, he accordingly dug down and found Mr. Sutliff, who was quite angry in being interrupted in this manner. Although perfectly sane on all other subjects, he continued digging almost every day for the greater part of his life, for a period of perhaps 30 or 40 years, till the infirmities of old age compelled him to desist."

Incidentally, speaking of turnpikes, Sutliff was the first parishioner who brought his family to meeting at Plymouth Center in a wheeled vehicle, a long wagon that creaked slowly up the long hill.

In 1809 Eli began to scent gold, but not under the turnpike. He made his remaining three thousand clock movements for the Porters, and for all that anyone has discovered to the contrary, he got paid. This was the year that Silas Hoadley went to work for Eli. Clocks were sold for a little while under the firm name of Terry, Thomas and Hoadley.

That was the first of the bewildering changes in partnership and location that distinguished Connecticut clock manufacture from then on. In 1810 Eli sold out to Thomas and Hoadley, and moved back to Plymouth Hill. Taking for example only our own acquaintances in Plymouth, Heman Clark (who had bought Eli's original water power) built a factory down-stream at Plymouth Hollow, and ran it for two years; then Thomas sold out to Hoadley at Ireland, which now became known as Hoadleyville, and bought Clark's factory at Plymouth Hollow, which eventually took the name of Thomaston. Eli Sr. next moved down to the Naugatuck. Some years later there were three Terry firms in Plymouth, run by five Terrys. Clock collectors have very nearly gone mad in their vain efforts to learn exactly when and what these simple little moves were. I can only remark that I have had no more luck than my betters.

CHAPTER II

Further Progress and Problems

THE clock business in 1810 was already starting to mush-
room. Even the highly fragmentary census of manufac-
tures taken that year reported "14,569 wooden clocks."
Another observer somewhere got the figure of 14,565, value
$122,955, for Connecticut alone. Quite likely Connecticut was the
only state that reported its clock output.

No one has thought to tell us what Eli was doing in the next
couple of years—except that he began suffering severely, for all
his temperance, from gout—, but in a manner of speaking we can
see. The part of his life that had been shaped by old Connecticut
was about over. Now came his turn, through inventiveness and the
influence of his personality on his workmen and neighbors, to shape
a new Plymouth, a new Litchfield County, largely a new Connecticut.

In 1811 he bought a house in Waterbury from the Porters,
probably as a speculation—or else he was taking out some of his
pay for the 4000 clocks in real estate. He must have been tinkering
with the plans for his mantel clock, getting the kinks out. It was
not the old Connecticut way to sell an imperfect article merely
because people would buy it. Whatever the iniquities of later
Connecticut peddlers as a whole, nobody ever associated any Terry
with basswood hams or wooden cucumber seeds.

The United States by now numbered seventeen, the center of
population had moved to a spot forty-nine miles northwest of
Washington, and so the establishment of the United States General
Post Office was a real necessity. It widened the correspondence of
Eli Terry and other eastern manufacturers, but for decades their
actual shipments still had to go through haphazard chains of for-
warding agents, all listed on the box.

Even the outpouring of cheap clocks from Litchfield County
had not yet made the noon mark obsolete. In 1811 the Yale College Observatory gave a signal by which a cannon was fired exactly
at noon in the New Haven public square so that the townsfolk

could get their noon marks right. Fifteen years later New Haven people were still trusting their noon marks, and looking askance at Eli and his mean time.

In 1812 the Terrys had their seventh child, a daughter, and Eli went to work in an experimental shop back at his first location, turning out further trial shelf clocks. The United States declared war against Great Britain on June 18, and the shooting began in leisurely fashion at sea the following day. New England, of course, bitterly opposed "Mr. Madison's war," which paralyzed Yankee shipping, and brought on the bombardment of the Connecticut shore and a successful British invasion of the District of Maine. Nantucket Island went so far as to declare itself neutral. The celebrated Hartford Convention of disgusted New Englanders, which took place in 1814 an easy day's journey from Eli's shop, was accused of aiming at the same thing in a bigger way, although actually the delegates cared more about preventing the election of further presidents from Virginia.

The clockmakers of Litchfield County, even in those hard times, were more interested in clock than in governmental machinery. It was 1813 or 1814 when Asa Hopkins, who had a shop four miles up the Naugatuck River from Plymouth Hollow, patented a machine that would cut the teeth on several wooden clock wheels in one operation by means of three shafts or mandrels. His was a good machine, and long in use, although gradually superseded by one that Eli invented with only one mandrel. In December of 1813 Seth Thomas, who had sold out to Hoadley at Ireland, bought Heman Clark's Plymouth Hollow shop and set up for himself.

John Sutliff the gold-mining miller must have felt rather foolish after he sold his grist mill to Eli. It was Eli, not Sutliff, who really struck gold at Sutliff's mill. He spent 1813 and 1814 fitting up a new shop—his second conversion of a grist mill into a clock factory. By the time the shop was ready, so was Eli's design for a mantel clock that really satisfied him.

Eighteen hundred and fourteen was a memorable year, both to Eli and to the country. Commodore Hardy bombarded Stonington, Conn., for four days in mid-August; before the end of the month the British burned Washington; in September the American Commodore MacDonough won the Battle of Lake Champlain, and Francis Scott Key wrote *The Star-Spangled Banner* to the erratic tune of a German drinking-song; the Hartford Convention met on the fifteenth of December, and on the twenty-fourth the war was officially ended by the Treaty of Ghent, although Andrew Jackson innocently won the Battle of New Orleans some weeks later. With the end of the war came the end of the embargoes. American markets were promptly flooded with imported goods, breaking down prices and shutting American factories. "It would almost frighten a man to see a five-dollar bill, they were so scarce."

But the Connecticut clock factories were not shut down, not by a long chalk. They were so active that competition cut the price of a tall-clock movement from ten dollars to five dollars. And then came Eli Terry and perfected his thirty-hour wooden-wheeled shelf clock, which, said one of his employees, "completely revolutionized the whole business. The making of the old-fashioned hang-up wood clock . . . passed out of existence." Several patents for machines to make wooden clock parts were issued on August 22, 1814, to Waterbury and Plymouth men who had probably contrived the equipment for use in Terry's shop. And in 1814 Eli Sr. started teaching the trade to fifteen-year-old Eli Jr. and thirteen-year-old Henry.

The clock design that made this possible called for a box case twenty inches high by fourteen wide and four deep. Some of the first clocks had no dial, only the hours painted on the glass, with the naked works in view behind. The next step was to put in a dial, but expose the escapement wheel, which poked through where in later models the second hand was. Finally all the works went into hiding behind painted wooden dials decorated by local specialists, many of them women.

From 1814 on Eli Sr. could stop worrying about demand, and start pursuing supply. He had launched a new industry by producing four thousand clocks in three years. Five years later he was producing six thousand a year at fifteen dollars apiece, complete with case.

Eli Sr. got a patent in 1816 for his 1814 shelf clock. This patent proved much more valuable, and accordingly more troublesome, than his first proud discovery.

Patents in those days were less respected than they are now, and rather differently understood. For instance, the portrait painter Chester Harding tells of coming from western New York as a youth to "sell the patent" in the state of Connecticut on a newly invented spinning-wheel head, and going back with money and "a surplus of fifty or sixty wooden clocks and several watches, which I had taken for the patent in different parts of the State." You sold local mechanics your design and know-how for what you could get, and there was an end of it. Naturally there were always those from whom you could get nothing, but it was seldom worth while to exercise your theoretical prerogative of suing them.

Eli really deserved the title of Senior by now; his eighth child, George, was born in early 1815. Otherwise the year passed without memorable private events. The end of the war brought more joy to the clockmakers than to the textile mills and other industries that the British manufacturers tried to throttle by dumping. For a time merchants and shipbuilders throve while manufacturers folded up; then tariff acts were lobbied through, and American industry began to boom again. Clocks, of course, were among the few industries that needed no protection: the British had never even dreamed of such output or such prices.

It was the winter of 1816 that Chauncey Jerome, a young cabinetmaker, went to work for Eli Sr., whom he wrote about and admired for the rest of a long life. Jerome, more like Seth Thomas than like Terry, always had his mind fixed chiefly on the case of a clock. "Mr. Terry," he wrote, "being a great mechanic had made many improvements in the way of making the cases. Under his direction I worked a long time at putting-up machinery and benches." This was at the new factory, built in 1815.

The patent for Eli's improved shelf clock came through on the twelfth of June, 1818. As often happens in the meanderings of history, Terry's product, the staple of all Connecticut clockmaking for more than twenty years, has become famous for the wrong reason. Every antique-collector brightens at the name, "Terry pillar-and-scroll-top case": the pillars and scroll are his assurance of a recognized and desirable article. Yet Eli never pretended to be a cabinetmaker, and he sold many movements to joiners like Jerome for casing in. Indeed Carl Drepperd, a leading writer on American clockmaking, upholds the view that Heman Clark, not Terry, designed the first pillar-and-scroll case. What Eli designed was a cheap, reliable, one-day wooden movement for a shelf clock, with half-seconds pendulum and some other features that were important then but don't mean very much except to clock experts now. All of Eli's patents deal with the works, and at most mention only the size of the case.

Anyway, Terry Sr. or Heman Clark or somebody adorned the box case of a shelf clock, in the Empire fashion of the time, with a scroll or bonnet false front on the top, and half-round turned pillars down the sides in front. This was the pillar-and-scroll case, which caught the public fancy immediately, and has held that of antique-collectors, at least, ever since. Practically every clockmaker in Connecticut, and even as far away as Pennsylvania and Ohio, rushed to pillar-and-scroll his cases.

Case-making, like dial-making, became a thriving business in itself. Jerome, for instance, set up independently at Plymouth in 1818, buying Eli's movements, casing them, and then selling the complete clocks. After three years of this he moved to Bristol, and built a case shop where he used the first circular saw in town—copied, no doubt, from Terry's which was the first in Plymouth.

Some other manufacturers had a different scheme. All their work was done in their own shops, with the individual departments managed by contractors.

Eli just ground away at movements. Apparently much of his product went to surrounding manufacturers who liked to make fancy boxes more than wheels.

His old-fashioned steady habits gave a foundation to his business that no disaster ever shook. He throve with the rest of the clock trade, and kept going when they overreached themselves. The year 1816, for instance, is still sometimes remembered as "eighteen-hundred-and-froze-to-death." There was ice and snow in each of the twelve months; horseshoe-pitchers in Plymouth wore greatcoats on the fourth of July; there was no corn at all, and perhaps half the usual crops of other kinds. Eighteen-seventeen was scarcely better, and a mass exodus from New England to the beckoning Ohio left abandoned farms and deserted villages behind it. No doubt many of the covered wagons had a Terry clock, packed carefully away in hopes it would survive the long, rough, wet journey.

The whole Litchfield County clock business boomed noisily despite the two cold years. On the second of October, 1818, Eli Sr.

sold a "shop right" to his old employee Seth Thomas to make Terry's Patent shelf clocks.

Although it is hard to be sure of the terms under which Thomas operated, a legal document drawn up for Eli some years later indicates that Thomas originally agreed to pay a royalty, which was afterward commuted to a lump sum of a thousand dollars.

The document says, ". . . in the year 1818 Seth Thomas of Plymouth, then being engaged in the business of Manufacturing the common wooden wheeled clocks and being wholly ignorant of (Terry's) . . . improved plan of making clocks & being desirous of obtaining a wright to use the same, (Terry) entered into a contract with sd Thomas . . . , by which the said Terry licensed & convey to the said Thomas the right to make and sell Clocks at one Factory & without a partner under said Patent and to transfer to one individual his said license & right to make and sell sd clocks, and also to make Clocks without cases, if the purchaser did not case them or sell or dispose of them within twenty five miles of said Plymouth, and the said Thomas agreed to pay sd Terry fifty cents for each clock he should so make, excepting that for the first Eight hundred which he should make including those which he had begun to make at the time of said contract the sd Thomas was to pay said Terry nothing . . ."

Thomas was soon making about as many clocks under his shop right as Eli: "The said Thomas went into the business of making said clocks & carried on said business extensively and manufactured fifteen thousand of said Clocks . . . and made great gains thereby and by means thereof became and was & is a man of great wealth."

The result for people less fortunate than Terry and Thomas was that clock movements in Plymouth were much more plentiful than money. Peddlers from the west like Harding willingly took them in trade; the people of Plymouth and Bristol actually used them as a sort of currency. For instance, when Chauncey Jerome got ready to move, he sold his house in Plymouth to Eli Sr. for a hundred mantel-clock movements, with dials, tablets (the painted glass panel that went below the dial), and weights, but no cases. Jerome made cases for these and 114 more, and paid the 214 complete clocks for a house, barn, and seventeen acres of land in Bristol.

Eli Sr.'s brother Samuel, from East Windsor, started a shop at

Plymouth in 1818 to handle overflow work, and by then Son Henry was in the firm with Eli. The style was Eli Terry & Sons from 1818 to 1824.

Eli Jr. was now beginning to be a person of substance also; he married a Plymouth girl in 1821, and he and his father "united with" the Plymouth Center church at the same time.

General business was bad again in 1820 and 1821, this time even taking a bite out of the clock boom. Most American manufacturers laid their troubles to the deluge of foreign merchandise, though of course the clockmaker suffered from this only at second hand. The high-tariff boys were some three years in crowding a second list of protective duties through Congress.

Eli just went steadily ahead making clocks. He got a patent on the twenty-sixth of May, 1823, for some improvements in wooden-wheeled clocks. The only difference you or I could see is that the pendulum now swung from dead center instead of from the left.

Apparently in 1822 he offered Seth Thomas a shop right to use the new improvements, "but sd Thomas doubted the utility of the same, and endeavoured to dissuade (Terry) from making said improvements or putting the same into use being content with the privileges and improvements he had already purchased . . . , and being unwilling to change his tools and machinery to enter upon said new manufacture." The tyranny of tooling-up was already making itself felt, not fifteen years after clockmaking had graduated from the saw-and-compass stage.

"And thereupon the sd Terry and sd Thomas mutually agreed that in lieu of the said sum of fifty cents for each clock . . . Terry would accept of one thousand Dollars from sd Thomas with interest thereon from the date of said agreement to pay sd fifty cents—and the said Thomas agreed to continue to make the movements of his clocks as he then made the same (viz.) on the 23rd February A.D. 1822, and that he would not make use of any of the improvements made by sd Terry after the 2nd day of October 1818."

It must have been during the hard times of the twenties that Eli Sr. (among other trials, his son James died in 1822, aged 18) paid a most unusual tribute to Eli Jr. If he had written up his Most Unforgettable Character, it would have been not his father

Eli Terry—Eight-Day All Brass Movement
Made in East Windsor—1793

Dial of Eight-Day illustrated on previous page. All Brass—Hand Engraved.
Probably originally silvered finished but later cleaned off by some over-
zealous and ununderstanding housewife.

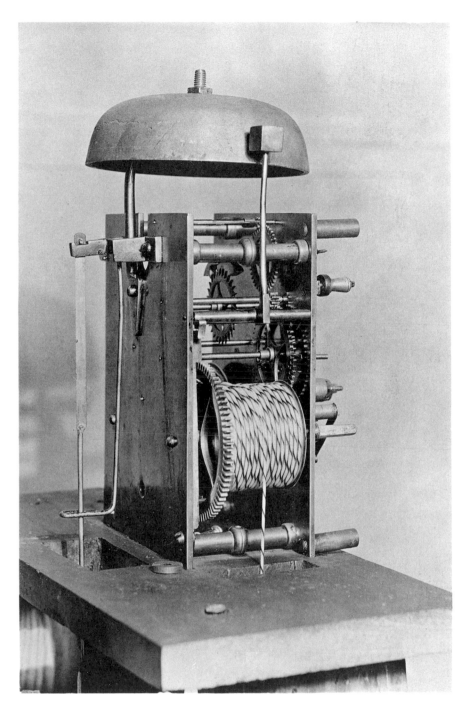

Movement of Eli Terry Eight-Day Clock pictured on previous pages.

Thirty-Hour Wood Movement built by Eli Terry.
Found in barn in Torringford.

Dial of clock illustrated on previous page. Probably
hand-decorated and designed by Terry himself.

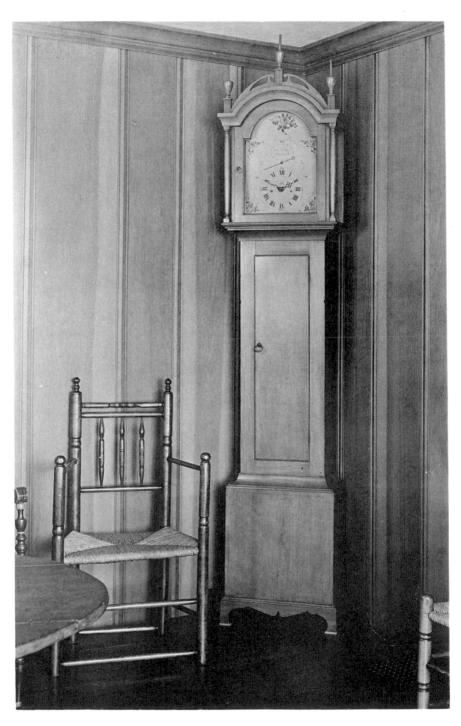

Eli Terry Tall Clock. Thirty-Hour Wood Movement. Case maker un-
known. Dial probably by Terry himself. Found in Northeast Harbor, Maine.

Dial of Clock illustrated on preceding page. Probably
designed and decorated by Eli Terry himself.

Regulator Type, Brass Movement, Eight-Day Clock by Eli Terry
His Last Clock, Circa 1850

Model of Shelf Clock by Eli Terry

Dial and Movement of Original Model Shelf Clock by Eli Terry

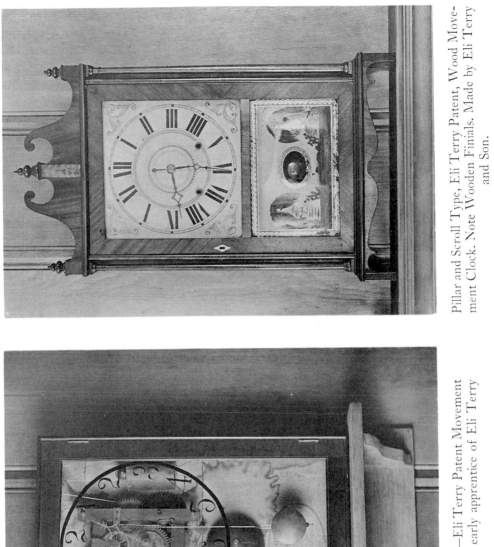

Pillar and Scroll Type, Eli Terry Patent, Wood Movement Clock. Note Wooden Finials. Made by Eli Terry and Son.

Open face Shelf Clock—Eli Terry Patent Movement Case by Seth Thomas, early apprentice of Eli Terry

Eli Terry Patent, Thirty-Hour Wood Movement.
Made by Eli Terry, Junior. Hitchcock Style Case.

Eli Terry & Son Mantel Clock

Home of Eli Terry which he built in Plymouth in 1793

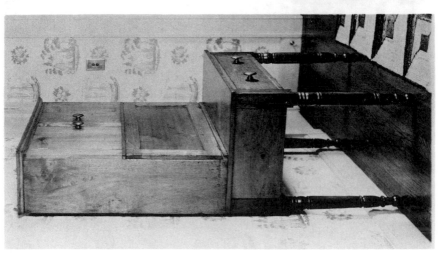

Bookkeeping Desk of Eli Terry, Jr.

Probable location of Eli Terry Shop on Niagara Brook, Plymouth
As it looks today. Old Shop long since gone

Old Mill Wheel built by Eli Terry, Jr. on brook opposite
Terry, Jr. Homestead at site of his clock shop, Terryville

Eli Terry, Sr. Tombstone
Old Cemetery—Terryville

Congregational Church—Terryville (Town of Plymouth),
Connecticut. Built in 1837. Eli Terry, Jr. (for whom Terry-
ville was named) was chief contributor to its building fund.
Note Clock Tower.

House first West of Congregational Church, Terryville, as now appears, built by Eli Terry. Presented to Church Society by O. D. Hunter for use as parsonage.

Eli Terry, Jr. Homestead. Terryville, Connecticut

but his eldest son: "I owe my success in life to his perseverance and help over difficulties which I had not power to surmount."

Eli Sr. became Grandpa Eli in 1823, when Eli Jr.'s first child was born and named James (after his recently dead young uncle). And in 1823, too, an industry launched at Waterbury twenty years before by Eli's old friend Levi Porter and his brother Abel finally grew to a size that brought a great change in clockmaking. Though cast brass wheels had been commonplace during Eli's apprenticeship, rolled sheet brass was a British monopoly. The Porters, then in the button business, contrived to roll some sheet brass with imported British machinery driven by a horse. Levi sold out in 1806 and made his dicker with Eli, and for nearly twenty years the American sheet-brass output remained trifling.

Then between 1820 and 1830 the sheet-brass mills, growing beyond mere button manufacture, had brass to spare for outsiders. Their neighbors the clockmakers were the first big customers.

Eli Sr., though he had created the wooden clock industry and remained faithful to it throughout his business career, was quite aware of the possibilities in brass. Some of his patents were drawn to cover brass as well as wooden movements. In 1822 he signed as a witness to a patent taken out by Joseph Ives of East Bristol on a looking-glass clock case. The movement that went in the case, also invented by Ives, had iron "plates"—the front and back framework—and brass wheels. These wheels were undoubtedly cast; the first sheet-brass wheels were cut from old kettles about 1825. It was not until 1832 that Joseph Ives perfected his eight-day movement made wholly of sheet brass. Since Eli Sr. was ready to retire, he did not convert his factory or cudgel his brains for a new model, but in later life he could and did invent a brass movement to order for Eli Jr.'s successors.

The twenties were full of bustle for all the Terrys no less than for the country. In 1824 Eli Jr., with the resolution his father so much admired, left Eli Terry & Sons and built a factory for himself on the Pequabuck River. Eli Sr. made a three-year partnership with his younger brother under the firm of Eli & Samuel Terry. Henry kept the old business, shortening its name to E. Terry & Sons.

About 1825 Chauncey Jerome changed the dimensions of the pillar-and-scroll case, gave it a lick of bronze paint, replaced the painted tablet with a mirror, and christened the result the "bronze looking-glass clock." This form held the field for several years; even the gruff and conservative Seth Thomas had to make bronze looking-glass clocks against his will.

On May 18 and September 9, 1825, Eli Sr. received patents on wooden-wheeled thirty-hour clocks. The first boats passed through the Erie Canal on the ninth of October, opening up the whole Middle West at one blow. Eli Jr., with his wife and two small sons, moved to the eastern part of Plymouth.

By this time Eli Sr. and Seth Thomas were each considered to be worth the staggering sum of a hundred thousand dollars. Eli could look philosophically upon the teapot tempest that followed in 1826.

A New Haven paper of June 13 reported that $250 had just been appropriated by the town meeting to buy a clock for the steeple of the Center Church. This put the seal of approval on an undertaking begun in January of 1824, when six pillars of New Haven society signed the following document: "The undersigned, Committee of the 1st Ecclesiastical Society of New Haven, give liberty to Mr. Eli Terry of Plymouth, to put up a clock in the Tower of the church belonging to said Society, provided the same be done at his expense and without injury to the building, and before the 1st of January 1825."

That was the usual procedure in buying a tower clock; the church merely gave leave to install one, and private citizens would find the money. In this particular case the town of New Haven was the buyer.

The time limit in Eli's agreement was extended once, and apparently again; the clock went to work, presumably, about the time when the $250 was raised.

At last Eli got some good out of his first patent: the New Haven tower clock showed mean time on one dial, apparent time on another. Eli wrote a letter of explanation to the newspapers, saying, in part, "Mean time is that which a clock would show provided it were perfect, made hours exactly of the same length, and came out right, at the end of every year. This is called 'Clock' in the almanac. Apparent time is that which is shown by the sun; and by this the days from noon to noon are not equal length, nor, of course, are the hours. There are not two days in the year of exactly the same length by the sun; and this is the reason why time thus measured, is denominated apparent time. . . .

". . . No clock, however perfect, can keep time with the sun, unless by means of additional and expensive apparatus. Those who attempt to keep apparent time with common clocks, must alter them not merely to correct their own deviations from equal motion, but also frequently to follow all the different variations of the sun through the year. . . ."

Eli's explanation, including the astronomy of the matter, was plain enough for anyone who would read it; but New Haven was far from satisfied. Yale College held its classes by the sun. Who was a clockmaker that he should teach lessons to Jehovah? Though Yale rejoiced in an older apparent-time clock built by one Simeon Jocelyn, Eli could not get away unchallenged with showing both kinds of time. An indignant letter-writer in the *Connecticut Journal* of November 14, signing himself "True Time," took the position that sun time was obviously correct time, and remarked tartly, "A public clock, which tells the truth, four times only in a year, is something very much like a public nuisance."

Three weeks later came a rejoinder from a Terry partisan: "If the faculty of Yale College find any convenience in regulating their exercises by the light of the sun, this may be done with perfect ease, by orders to the bell ringer. But surely the public at large ought not to have all their operations deranged, or their time-pieces injured, by attempts to follow the variations of apparent time."

"True Time" launched a long retort. Others joined in the fray without adding much to the argument. Perhaps what really hurt frugal Connecticut souls was the case reported in the *Columbian Register*: "A DEAD LOSS—In consequence of the late difference in our public Clocks, (about 20 minutes) it is said that an Irishman who had made a specific agreement for his rations demanded and actually obtained from his employer two *eleven o'clockers* in one forenoon. It is hoped that the Clocks will be soon regulated, so as to prevent the repetition of such an unhappy occurrence."

Eli's defense of his clock was confined to the one explanatory letter; he had to think much more about defending his business in another quarter. The shelf-clock movement in its ultimate form suited both manufacturer and buyer to perfection. There almost seemed to be no other way of making it but Eli's way. Naturally, then, those clockmakers who were not inventors but mechanics— about ninety-eight per cent—made what were really Terry clocks. Sometimes they gave a nod to the patent law by some perfunctory change; the numerous "woodshed clockmakers" never even bothered, rightly thinking themselves too small to be worth suing. Eli was in a little the same fix as Whitney with the cotton gin—his invention was so obviously Heaven-sent that people could not believe it was private property.

But unless it was private property, where did Eli come in?

With true Terry inventiveness, he entered a lawsuit on September 2, 1826, in the U.S. Circuit Court, not against the real pirates, but against his old apprentice, partner, and neighbor Seth Thomas. He charged Thomas with infringing his amended patents granted March 4 and July 5, 1826. In April of 1827 he brought a similar suit before the Superior Court that was to sit at Litchfield in August. He then charged Thomas with making at least 16,000 clocks in violation of agreement over a period of five years.

This looks a little startling at first glance, especially since Thomas had paid good money for his original shop right, and remained on the best of terms with Terry. But that was the whole point: Eli sued a good friend so as to spread dismay among copyists, and the friend would not force him to the trouble and expense of pushing the suit.

The suits either served their purpose or else, more likely, did not; Eli quietly discontinued the first in April, 1829. His time as a large-scale manufacturer was growing short, and Eli Jr. took the commercial department more and more into his own hands.

The next few years, barring gout, were placid for Eli Sr. The Eli Jrs. had a daughter in 1827. The forty-one-per-cent "Tariff of Abominations" that Daniel Webster's men drove through in 1828 will hardly have excited the clockmakers, though it made their southern customers very angry. In the unlikely event that they heard about the Pittsburgh man who patented a clock with glass wheels in 1830, hard-riding ex-peddlers like the Terrys must have split their sides. As well have glass wheels on a wagon!

The Eli Jrs. had another child in 1830, and lost him before he was a year old.

Perhaps 1831 brought some small offset in the shape of public recognition. The village in eastern Plymouth where Eli Jr. had his shop took the name of Terrysville (the *s* was dropped in the 'seventies). The post office of that name opened three days before Christmas, with one of Eli Jr.'s numerous business connections as postmaster. (The spoils system was not yet in full swing, since the first recorded compensation to the Terrysville postmaster was $22.88 for the year 1833.) Mail stages ran three times a week from Litchfield by way of Plymouth and Terrysville to Hartford.

In 1831, also, Eli Jr.'s younger brother Silas—"Burnham" to the family—opened a clock shop at the fork of the Pequabuck and Poland rivers. Burnham supplied clocks to Eli Jr. in rush periods, and tinkered with his own inventions. He had a lot of ideas more ingenious than useful, but was no merchant. In later life he worked for other clockmakers, finally confounding the confusion of Terry clock genealogy with one last concern simply called the Terry Clock Company.

The Eli Jrs. were unfortunate again: their fifth child, born in March, died in early September. Burnham got married in November.

Eighteen hundred and thirty-two also brought the beginning of another revolution in clockmaking. Joseph Ives of Bristol invented his eight-day movement made of rolled brass. Of course the revolution was not immediately apparent; wooden clocks held the field for several years more. But even by 1835 brass clocks were worth mentioning in the total of 100,000 produced within the year by the three towns of Bristol, Plymouth, and Farmington.

Something of a revolution disturbed the country at large. That was the year when Andrew Jackson was re-elected, and when South Carolina undertook for its own convenience to nullify the federal tariff. Another year, and Jackson was sharpening his knife for the Bank of the United States: the Era of Good Feeling was forgotten.

For Eli Sr., however, perhaps it is not too much to say that it never ended. In 1833 he went out of business as a manufacturer, turning over his customers to Eli Jr. In spite of piracy, speculation, hard times, and disgruntled southern customers, he had accumulated by the age of sixty-one a fortune that yielded him an income of three thousand a year for the rest of his days. Enough is as good as a feast, he probably remarked to the friends who kept frantically seeking paper fortunes in wooden clocks.

The real fortune lay in doing as you pleased, driving clocks instead of being driven by them, and being Uncle Eli to all Plymouth. His old calling was his new hobby; now he could spend all the time he pleased fooling around his home clock shop, and so far as I can learn that was the chief thing he did for the next seventeen or eighteen years.

The addition of his father's customers spurred Eli Jr. to branch out. He bought up the machinery and stock of a derelict cabinet-lock business in Watertown, moved it to Terrysville, and formed Lewis, McKee & Company (himself, Postmaster John C. Lewis of Terrysville, and his own brother-in-law William McKee) to make locks. Since the labor and some of the operations required were about the same as for sheet-brass clocks, the new industry promptly made itself at home in Terrysville. Many of the managers and workmen shifted or alternated between clocks and locks. It must be said, however, that Eli Jr. encountered here an obstacle quite new to him, British competition; profitable lockmaking remained for his successors to accomplish.

The sixth child of the younger Eli Terrys was a daughter, who happily did not share the fate of the two little brothers preceding her.

Eli Sr., of course, had not gone a-peddling for years; Eli Jr. kept on after his father gave up, but now his growing family and spreading business ventures kept him at home. Besides, a change was coming over peddling. The makers had long since stopped loading their output on horseback, or even into their own wagons. Peddling was a full-time trade. The market expanded west and south, while canals, steamboats, and the first tentative railroads made it possible to ship clocks by the case instead of the saddle-load. The Farmington Canal, which ran through Plainville down to New Haven, opened for business in 1831, providing cheap transport to the sea except when the water in the canal was low. And some of the big southern peddlers, such as Birdseye Pickett of Knoxville, came to Terrysville with fleets of wagons driven by slaves.

The commercial morals of the Yankee peddlers had horrified the godly even in Eli's peddling days; by the 'thirties and 'forties "peddler" was an epithet akin to "vagrant." One Connecticut clock peddler in Illinois complained, "I doubt whether Henry has quite brass enough to Peddle Clocks. I will try him next month, and if we are compelled to hire another man to come out from Connecticut I hope he will not be one that will feel above his business. . . . Henry is too chicken hearted or he would have sold half the clocks before now . . . and Hopkins loves Girls much better than wooden clocks."

"It is a profound tribute," writes a modern commercial historian, "to the quality of the wares of many early manufacturers such as Eli Terry . . . that their industries managed to survive the ministrations of Sam Slick and his fraternity."

Yet Eli Sr.'s steady habits had not collapsed while he was on the road with his own clocks. Eli Jr. may have talked faster and smoother, but he too was selling an article that he knew to be good. Chauncey Jerome represented the next step: most of the clocks he sold were made by Terry and others, and merely cased by himself.

As the output, the competition, and the pressure for sales grew, so did the number of peddlers, while the peddler's sense of responsibility for his wares became even slighter.

Some were fly-by-night rascals like the legendary character who sold worthless alarm clocks (Eli Jr., incidentally, would add an alarm to any of his clocks for seventy-five cents), promising to replace any that did not work. When his stock got down to one clock, he would retrace his route, giving each disgusted purchaser a new dud for the old one, and then vanish forever into another state.

Other distributors, again, were responsible merchants who hired and sent out peddlers from a fixed headquarters. One of these, James Brice of Washington, Pa., became so important to the Terrys that Eli Jr.'s son Andrew clerked in a store at Washington, and married a girl from there.

The surviving letter books of Eli Terry Jr. & Company show that the honest salesmen of Terry clocks greatly outnumbered possible sharpers. There was real concern in Terrysville over clocks that would not run: complaints brought prompt and anxious inquiries. One peddler was instructed to clear off a dubious lot at reduced prices. "Warranted if well used" over the Terry name carried an actual promise.

But sharp practice was by no means all on the side of the peddlers. "Clock warrants" caused difficulties because the purchasers used any trouble with the clock as an excuse for not meeting their notes; the firm had to draw up a new form of note that closed the loophole. Even so, clock notes ranked far below flour, nails, or droves of hogs as acceptable pay. A hundred-pound shoat would pay for an ordinary clock at wholesale prices.

The shoat, furthermore, might be refractory, but he was pay in hand. Clockmakers who insisted on money transactions had to give one and often two years' credit, and peddlers did the same for their customers. Real, hard money on the barrel-head brought a discount of from six to ten per cent off wholesale clock prices— hard money, because wildcat bank bills were almost as bad as clock notes. The modern businessman who feels that the government is questionnairing him out of business should take a look at what too little government did to his great-grandfather. Andrew Jackson killed the Bank of the United States in 1833, and for the next few years live hogs were about the least troublesome kind of currency.

In 1835 Virginia, followed by South Carolina and Georgia, deliberately tried to tax the odious Yankee peddlers and their goods out of business. Peddlers' licenses had been required here and there for a century or more; New York collected nearly two thousand dollars for licenses in 1828, Georgia nearly twelve hundred; Pennsylvania and Virginia each took in over three thousand in 1831. But in 1835 Virginia multiplied her tax on all peddlers who sold goods made outside the state. No Connecticut clocks were wanted, please.

Chauncey Jerome thereupon showed what a Yankee peddler could do when roused. Made in Virginia? Simple—Chauncey and his brother Noble packed up cases of disassembled clock parts at Bristol, and sent them down with a few workmen to put them together in Richmond. Seth Thomas followed suit with a dummy firm in Augusta, Georgia. For a year or so the business in "southern-made" clocks flourished, to the delight of local-patriot planters.

Then two-year credits and wildcat banking caught up with the clockmakers and everyone else. The panic of 1837 mowed clockmakers down in rows. "We really thought that clocks would no longer be made," said Jerome. Eli Jr.'s brother Henry quit clock-making for the woolen business. The most frequent remark in the letter books is, "Please send our Mr. Eli Terry Jr. some money." A letter to the chief Terry peddler in Ohio in 1838 said, "Our object in writing to you at this time is to state our necessity. We are in debt to our workmen and they have got in debt to others for provisions & the necessities of life, & they must be paid or they cannot work, we have put them off as long as it will do & now they must be paid. They cannot get trusted unless they pay up once in about a year, & the time has come."

Eli Sr., of course, was happily concerning himself with the construction of split-second "regulator" timepieces for watch-makers (worth from one to two hundred dollars apiece) and tower clocks of his new design. Eli Jr. had to devise more fool-proof collection methods than foolproof clock movements, but even so he remembered his duty to God and society. In 1838 the Terrysville Congregational Church was built on a piece of land given by Eli Jr., who also gave nearly a third of the $3558 raised to put up the building. Father and son transferred from the Ply-mouth Hill to the Terrysville church. Eli Sr. built a house just west of it, and moved in for the rest of his life.

The last of 1839 was a dark time for both the Terrys. Eli Jr. had to start closing down the business and selling off his clocks "for want of funds," and on the fifteenth of December his mother, Eunice Warner Terry, died after forty-four years of marriage and nine children.

To make matters worse, Eli Jr.'s health began to fail. Between this and the hard times, he saw more attractions in farming than in clockmaking. Furthermore the wooden-clock business was just about done for. In 1838 Chauncey Jerome had picked up a Ger-man brass clock movement in the South, and he suddenly realized that by a few small changes he could produce a thirty-hour, that is a one-day, clock of rolled brass. The Ives brass movement had been eight-day. Jerome's new adaption was a clock cheaper and, for the price, more durable than any the world had ever seen. But at the same time it took more capital to make. The Jerome bro-thers, soon to be at the crest of their prosperity, started turning out thirty-hour brass movements in huge quantities.

The Terry firm could only follow suit. For some time they

supported the sale of brass clocks by the familiar tie-in method, refusing to sell wooden clocks (whose price was depressed by competition) unless the dealer also bought brass. In 1839, when Eli Jr. was withdrawing from clockmaking, his partner, one of the innumerable Plymouth Blakesleys, planned to carry on the business in nothing but thirty-hour brass movements.

As for Seth Thomas, Jerome said that he perhaps "hated as bad as anyone did to change his whole business of clockmaking for the second time, and adopt the same thing that I had introduced . . . he was highly incensed at me because I was the means of his having to change."

Eli Jr. and the clock business might be flagging, but not Uncle Eli. In November of 1840 (the year his son George graduated from Yale) he married Widow Harriet Peck (who was, incidentally, an aunt of Major J. B. Pond, the pioneer lecture manager).

In 1840, too, Eli Jr.'s eighth child, Eli Terry III, was born.

Eli Jr. scarcely lived to make his acquaintance, for he died at Terrysville on the twenty-first of May, 1841, at only 41. Four days later his sister Huldah died in New York; Eli Sr. must have felt very old indeed. Another daughter married a central New York farmer that year.

The two houses he had built in Terrysville were more than roomy enough now. In August he gave one of them to the Terrysville Congregational Church as a parsonage. It must have been about then, also, that he gave the church its tower clock, which still keeps time for Terrysville. Built on an improved system that defied wind and weather, it kept mean time only; no complaints from sun-worshippers have been preserved.

After Eli Jr. died, his company, what remained of it, was sold to the brothers Hiram and Heman Welton, under the style of Hiram Welton & Co. They carried on Milo Blakesley's plan of making thirty-hour brass clocks.

The new generation of Plymouth clockmakers, however, were not the mechanics their fathers had been. The Weltons copied exactly Jerome's copy of the stray German movement on which the Jerome business was built. Jerome sued them.

Uncle Eli, that venerable relic of an earlier Connecticut, still had the answers even in the age of brass. The Weltons asked him to invent a thirty-hour brass movement that would be proof against Jerome's lawsuits. That was no great task for a man who in his teens had threaded his own brass screws and drawn his own wire. So any collector who has a Welton brass clock that is not just like a Jerome movement may congratulate himself on possessing the last product of Eli Terry Sr.'s ingenuity. (The last clock he ever *built*, one of the unique rarities belonging to his great-great-grandson Charles Terry Treadway, has never been out of the family; but it is a normal "regulator," not a new invention.)

If I call Eli Sr. a venerable relic, I refer only to his years. His tenth child, the first by Harriet Peck Terry, was born in June of 1842. Another, who died in boyhood, followed in November of 1843.

Eighteen forty-two was the year when Jerome first began exporting his brass clocks to England. The British customs officers at first thought dollar-and-a-half clocks must be some shifty Yankee form of dumping; but Jerome kept pouring them out as fast as he could sell them—very fast indeed—, and making money on the deal. He even began eyeing India and China. In another two years his firm moved from Bristol to New Haven, where it eventually came a cropper by tangling with a Connecticut Yankee of the newer wooden-nutmeg style, P. T. Barnum.

Uncle Eli had always been a strict temperance man. The whole great American temperance movement germinated at Plymouth on the fifth of September, 1810, when Lyman Beecher was startled by the drinking that went on at the ordination of the Reverend Luther Hart. Beecher was then preaching in Litchfield. "None of the Consociation were drunk," said Beecher; "but that there was not, at times, a considerable amount of exhilaration, I can not affirm." A generation later the movement had grown enough so that a cousin of Eli's first wife opened a temperance hotel at Terrysville. He must have enjoyed Eli's active support, for in addition to his teetotalism he was a strong adherent of Eli's pet new Congregational church.

The shadows were lengthening. Another daughter died in 1844; in 1845 Hiram Welton & Co. failed despite the clock Eli had invented for them. The Mexican War and the gold rush kept people too busy to think about old men who had once made wooden clocks in the Connecticut hills. In 1849 Silas Hoadley, long since "the Honorable," retired and rented his shop to a cutlery maker. According to the definitive historian of Connecticut clockmaking, Penrose Hoopes, 1850 marked the final eclipse of the wooden clock. In 1851 Harriet Pond Peck Terry died; a month later, September 24, Eli made his will.

On the twenty-fourth day of February, 1852, having created and outlived an industry, Eli Terry Sr. went to his reward.

The clockmaking equipment listed in the inventory of his effects might have come from half a century before—as indeed perhaps most of it had:

1 hand vice	$1.00	1 hone	$1.00
1 stake and hammer	2.50	1 stovepipe and tongs	.50
brace and bitts	3.00	1 beam compass	1.00
1 shaving knife	.25	2 iron saw frames	1.00
1 panel saw	.50	1 small brace	.50
1 hack saw	.75	1 lot small clock tools	1.88
2 hand vices	.67	1 hand drill	.50
1 small bench vise	.50	2 pair compasses	1.00
8 pair plyers	1.00	1 pair calipers	.50
1 engine and fixtures	20.00	1 lot reamers &c.	.50
4 drill stocks	1.00	1 try square	.25
files and tools	5.50	1 rotary clock movement	.50
1 pair large shears	1.00	1 grindstone	.30
1 stake and steel screw driver	.50	1 case watch tools entire	8.00
1 set planes	3.00	1 level	.50
1 unfinished clock with case	5.00	1 magnifying glass	1.00
		3 augers	1.50
1 unfinished clock movement	1.50	1 hatchet	.33
1 balance clock	2.00	1 anvil	2.00
1 clock in garret	1.00	2 hammers	.50
cold chisels &c.	.25	forge tools	.75
1 wire guage	.25	2 small hammers	.50
oil stones and hone	1.00	1 2 ft. rule	.12
2 brass turning lathes, chuck drills and turning tools	20.00	cold chisels	.17
		1 clock	.50
		1 scraper	.13
		1 bellows	5.00
1 grindstone	.50	1 pair scales to weigh gold	.50

As the Weltons and many others since have found out, there is no mechanical substitute for a man like Eli Terry.

The growth of the Connecticut clock business sprang directly from Terry, and clockmaking in Bristol, Thomaston, and Waterbury is a huge industry today. But Terry produced at one remove even greater industrial developments.

His grandson Andrew (son of Eli Jr.) and his wife's cousin G. F. Warner each did very well with a malleable iron foundry.

His son Henry, after quitting the clock business in the panic of 1837, operated a woolen mill at Plymouth.

His grandson James first experimented with exotic varieties of mulberry during the silkworm craze of the early 'forties, then took over Eli Jr.'s lock firm, Lewis, McKee & Company. After clock manufacture in Terrysville stopped, James Terry's Eagle Lock Company became the chief industry of the village and a dominant firm in the lock business.

You have already seen how Ives and Jerome clocks multiplied the market for rolled brass, accounting in good part for the early expansion of such monster firms as the present Scovill and the Benedict & Burnham manufacturing companies.

Spring-driven clocks had many advantages of convenience over the weight-powered kind; but spring-powered clocks called for huge quantities of finely tempered springs, which could only be imported from France. Until American springs were forthcoming, inexpensive clocks had to keep their weights.

A young Bristol clockmaker named Dunbar decided to supply the springs; Silas Burnham Terry had invented a process to do the tempering in quantity. Dunbar and Terry made the following agreement: "In consideration of five hundred dollars to me in hand paid, I hereby promise to impart to Edward L. Dunbar, Lorenzo D. Jacobs, Winthrop Warner all the information I possess by telling and showing them how to harden and temper clock springs for the purpose that said Dunbar, Jacobs and Warner may make clock springs to sell to all persons who may wish to purchase the same except Chauncey Jerome of New Haven and I also agree not to impart to any other person or persons the information that I possess of making clock springs, reserving to myself the privilege of learning a person or persons to harden and temper stock springs for self-adjusting stocks provided I take from him or them a bond not less than five hundred dollars not to make clock springs, and also reserving to myself the right of using said art for my own purposes, and I also agree that if said

Dunbar, Jacobs and Warner shall wish to learn any other person or persons to make clocksprings for themselves they shall have the privilege of learning such persons only on condition that they make such springs or use said art for said Dunbar, Jacobs and Warner and also that such persons so learning sign a bond to said Dunbar, Jacobs and Warner that they will not use said art or make clock springs for any persons whatsoever.

—Silas B. Terry"

Eli Terry III engaged in the spring business; and Wallace Barnes, another great spring-maker, was first a partner and then a successor to Dunbar. The present Associated Spring Corporation embodies these and several later concerns.

The most roundabout progress from a clockmaking start is that of the modern New Departure Company Division of General Motors. Two young southerners who had invented a patent doorbell were driven north by an epidemic of yellow fever. The bell required a simple form of clock escapement, and so obviously Connecticut was the place to buy it. They picked Bristol for their plant.

From doorbells they went to bicycle bells; from bicycle bells to bicycle coaster-brakes; from coaster-brakes to ball bearings; and so to a multi-million-dollar corporation.

It was much simpler after all than even the first of Eli Terry's wooden clocks.

THE END

ૐ

"Actorum Memores simul affectamus Agenda!"

A NEWCOMEN BOOK

THIS SMALL BOOK *is one of a series issued occasionally by The Newcomen Society in North America, dealing with the extensive subject of Material History in the United States of America and in Canada. The Society believes that the colorful and often dramatic story of courageous and pioneer efforts within the fields of Industry, Invention, Engineering, Transportation, Communication, the Utilities, Agriculture, Mining, Finance, Banking, Economics, Education, and the Law—the history of these—serves many times as a source of inspiration for the present and as a guide for the future. It is in this spirit, as constituting an informal contribution to the broad and interesting subject of Material History, that this small book is issued.*

*"Actorum Memores simul
affectamus Agenda!"*